This book
belongs to:
BeNEvans

CARTOON NETWORK ™

CONTENTS

Published by Pedigree Books Limited
The Old Rectory, Matford Lane, Exeter EX2 4PS

Pedigree® BOOKS

£6.99
CN1

ON YOUR MARKS!

Take your seats, for the race is about to begin. Before it starts, though, see if you can match up these Wacky Racers to their vehicles. If you need a jump start, the answers are at the bottom of the page!

1

A

2

B

3

C

4

D

5

E

Answers: 1-D, 2-E, 3-B, 4-C, 5-A.

Wacky Racers ™ -IN- **DRAG RACING**

MICHAEL KRAIGER
STORY
BILL ALGER
PENCILS
ANDREW PEPOY
INKS
PHIL FELIX
LETTERS
DAVE TANGUAY
COLORS
BRONWYN TAGGART
EDITS

PODUNK POWDERPUFF RALLY

WE'RE HERE TODAY AT PODUNK'S ANNUAL POWDER PUFF RALLY, WHERE THE WINNER ISN'T NECESSARILY THE FASTEST RACER, BUT THE DRIVER WHO BEST COMPLETES THE WACKY RALLY COURSE!

SAY, WHAT'S THIS?

AREN'T YOU FINISHED YET, MUTTLEY?

OH, NO! IT'S THE DIRTY-DEALING DICK DASTARDLY AND HIS SIDEKICK, MUTTLEY. WHAT'S THAT TROUBLESOME TWOSOME DOING HERE? DON'T THEY KNOW THAT THIS RACE IS JUST FOR *GIRLS*?

HOME SWEET HOME

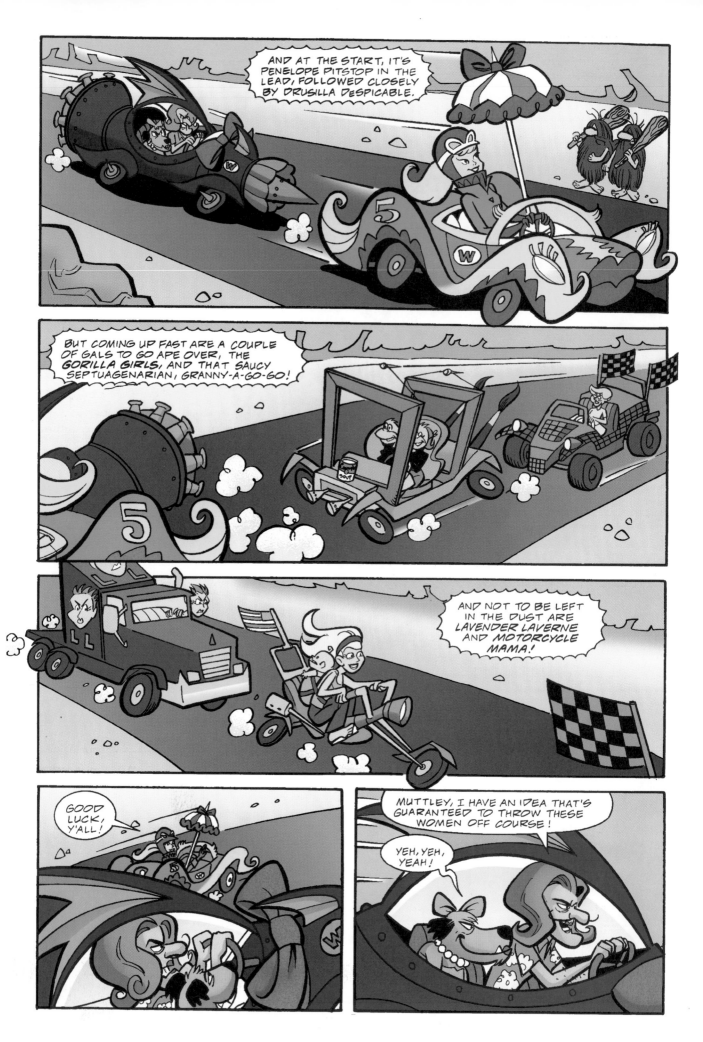

I'M LOOKING FOR THE RALLY DIRECTIONS AND SOME SENSIBLE SHOES!

Hmm... I'LL NEED ONE OF EACH, IN PINK.

HEEK, HEEK, HEEK, HEE!

POIT!

THUNK!

BUMP!

THUD!

QUIT DRAGGING YOUR FEET, MUTTLEY! NOW'S OUR CHANCE TO STEP ON IT!

DRAT, DRAT, DOUBLE DRAT! HOW DID SHE ESCAPE OUR FANCY FOOT-WORK!

IN THE SECOND LEG OF THE RALLY, THE *GORILLA GIRLS*—WHO DON'T WEAR SHOES—HAVE TAKEN THE LEAD.

NOW TO SET THE PERFECT TRAP FOR THOSE ANNOYING APES! MUTTLEY, GIVE ME A QUARTER!

THAT'S RIGHT, OFFICER, TWO WILD GORILLAS HAVE ESCAPED FROM THE CIRCUS! THEY WERE LAST SEEN HEADING WEST!

HEEK, HEEK, HEE...

A FEW MINUTES LATER...

PODUNK ANIMAL CONTROL UNIT

PATROL

GOOD DAY, LADIES!

TA-TA, BOYS!

FRAZZA RAZZA, RAM FRAZZA!

THE LAST TWO RACERS CROSS THE FINISH LINE AS THE WINNER'S TROPHY IS PRESENTED TO -- DRUSILLA DE'SPICABLE!

SKRITTCH!

MATCHES

FWOOOSH!

HEEK-HEEK-HEEK-HEEK-HEE!

FA-WHOOOOM!

IT LOOKS LIKE THE REAL WINNER OF PODUNK'S POWDER PUFF RALLY IS PENELOPE PITSTOP!

I JUST KNEW LITTLE OL' SHE WAS A HE, WHEN SHE PASSED UP THE GORGEOUS PUMPS ON SALE AT THAT SHOE STORE!

THE END!

A Shady Character

All these shadows of the devious Dick Dastardly look the same, but only one matches the picture exactly. Which one is the real Dick Dastardly? The answer is at the bottom of the page.

SHOP TILL YOU DROP

Judy Jetson is going to a party tonight and is out shopping for an outfit. She started at shop number 1, then visited shops 2,3,4 and 5. Now she's on her way back to shop 1 to buy her outfit! If there are eight space miles between each shop, and shop 1 is five space miles from home, how many space miles has Judy travelled altogether on her shopping trip? The answer is at the bottom of the page.

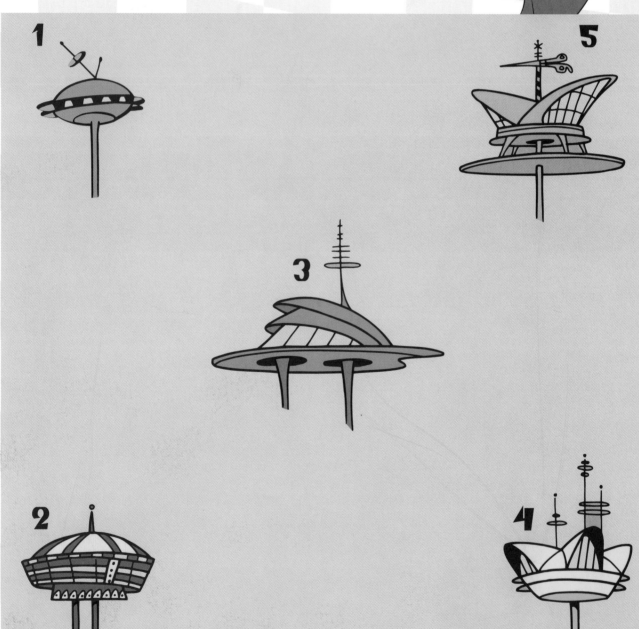

22

THE Jetsons™ IN ROBO-GEORGE

WELL, WHAT DO YOU THINK OF THE NEW ROBOT?

I DON'T BELIEVE IT!

Story: **Michael Kupperman**
Pencils: **Bill Wray**
Inks: **Stephen DeStefano**
Letters: **Jon Costanza**
Color: **Bernie Mireault**
Edits: **Bronwyn Taggart**
Special Thanks To Mike Brisbois

IT LOOKS JUST LIKE ME!

WELL, EXACTLY!

NOW I'LL HAVE TWO JETSONS TO YELL AT AND ORDER AROUND! IT'S GONNA BE *GREAT!*

JETSON, THIS IS PROFESSOR MUELLER, THE *INVENTOR* OF THE ROBOT. HE'S GOING TO NEED YOU TO ANSWER A LOT OF QUESTIONS ABOUT YOURSELF, SO THAT HE CAN PROGRAM IT CORRECTLY!

HELLO DERE!

NOW, IT IS VERY IMPORTANT THAT YOU DO NOT LIE--YOU MUST TELL ZEE *ABSOLUTE* TRUTH.

OH-OKAY!

FIRST OF ALL—HOW DO YOU LIKE YOUR JOB?

OH! UM...

I LOVE IT! IT'S HARDLY LIKE WORKING AT ALL, I ENJOY IT SO MUCH!

REALLY? OK! AND YOUR BOSS, MR. SPACELY?

UH—HE'S A GREAT GUY! I LOVE HIM! IT'S A PLEASURE TO BE WORKING FOR HIM!

HUH! I CAN'T SAY I'M SURPRISED!

*T*WO HOURS LATER...

WOW! I TOLD SO MANY *LIES!* BUT I COULDN'T GIVE THE CORRECT ANSWERS— MR. SPACELY WOULD HAVE *FIRED* ME!

SPACELYS SPACE SPROCKETS

LAB

THE NEXT DAY... NOW ZAT WE HAVE PROGRAMMED ZEE ROBOT WITH ALL ZEE UTTERLY TRUTHFUL ANSWERS ZAT MR. JETSON HAS GIVEN--

--WE ARE READY TO OBSERVE ZEE ROBOT, WHO IS ALREADY HARD AT WORK!

IF EVERYTHING HAS WORKED OUT RIGHT, HE SHOULD BE BEHAVING *JUST LIKE* MR. JETSON!

CLICK!

I DON'T UNDERSTAND!

I THOUGHT HE WAS SUPPOSED TO BE JUST LIKE JETSON! JETSON'S NEVER WORKED THIS HARD A DAY IN HIS LIFE!

ZERE MAY HAVE BEEN AN ERROR IN ZEE INFORMATION I WAS GIVEN.

UH... UH...

LOOK AT HIM! HE'S FANTASTIC! IF HE ALWAYS WORKS THIS HARD, I CAN *GET RID* OF THE ORIGINAL!

BUT-- BUT--

WELL, THE WORKDAY IS ALMOST DONE! NOW VEE SHOULD OBSERVE ZEE ROBOT AT HOME—*YOUR HOME!* MAYBE ZERE IT WILL BEGIN TO ASSUME YOUR CHARACTER- ISTICS!

FACE IT, JETSON! THE ROBOT'S BETTER THAN YOU IN EVERY WAY!

YAH, IT WOULD APPEAR SO!

UND IT IS BECAUSE YOU LIED— IT ACTUALLY RESULTED IN THE ROBOT BEING A *SUPERIOR* VERSION OF YOU!

IT'S NOT FAIR!

WHAT'S FAIR GOT TO DO WITH IT? LOOK—NOW HE'S DANCING THE MINUET WITH YOUR WIFE!

YES—HE MOVES SO GRACEFULLY!

LATER...

WELL, YOUR FAMILY IS ALL ASLEEP NOW, HAPPY AND CONTENT. WE SHALL TAKE ZEE ROBOT BACK WITH US AND PUT IT IN STORAGE FOR ZEE NIGHT.

THAT'S RIGHT! TOMORROW WE'LL DISCUSS OUR PLANS FOR THE FUTURE. SLEEP WELL, JETSON!

IF ONLY I'D TOLD THE TRUTH, THAT HUNK OF JUNK WOULD BE AS USELESS AS *I* AM!

NEXT MORNING...

NOW WE MUST ASK THE ROBOT HOW HE FELT ABOUT HIS EXPERIENCES.

THE ROBOT HAS *FEELINGS*?

OH, YES — HE HAS THE FEELINGS THAT RESULT FROM THE PERCEPTIONS THAT HE HAS BEEN MAKING, FILTERED THROUGH THE PERSONALITY GRID THAT WE HAVE CONSTRUCTED FOR HIM!

OH, I SEE!

I WILL ACTIVATE HIM — ZO!

CLICK!

SO, ROBOT— HOW DO YOU LIKE BEING GEORGE JETSON? IS IT REALLY YOUR IDEAL LIFE, AS YOU HAVE BEEN SAYING?

NO!

I HATE IT! THIS JOB IS AWFUL!

AND THAT LITTLE MAN, MR. SPACELY— WHAT'S HE SUPPOSED TO BE?

SOME KIND OF GARGOYLE, OR TROLL?

HE'S AN IDIOT!

HE CALLED ME A GARGOYLE! AND A TROLL! AND AN *IDIOT*!

SCIENCE CLASS

Elroy is studying robots as part of his science project. How many complete robots like the one here can he build with the parts below? The answer is at the bottom of the page.

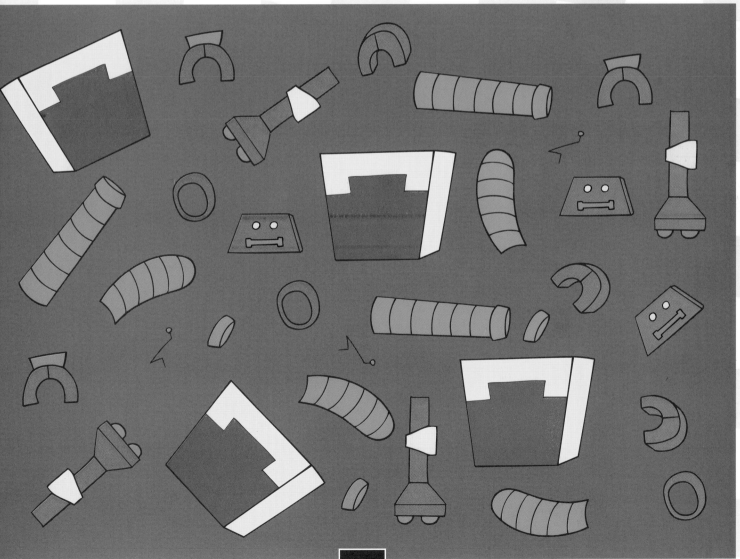

Answer: Elroy can build 3 complete robots.

STONE AGE SCULPTURE

Oops! Fred was just putting the finishing touches to his stone sculpture when he tapped a little too hard. Now his masterpiece is smashed to bits! See if you can work out which Flintstone character he had been working on. The answer is at the bottom of the page.

32

GOODBYE, WILMA. REMEMBER, I'VE GOT *BOWLING PRACTICE* AFTER WORK.

ALL RIGHT, FRED. HAVE A GOOD DAY.

THE FLINTSTONES ™ IN **THE AGONY OF DE FEET**

SAM HENDERSON—WRITER
GLEN HANSON—PEN ILLER
MIKE DeCARLO—INKER
KEN LOPEZ—LETTERER
MIKE BRISBOIS—ASSISTANT ED.
BRONWYN TAGGART—EDITOR
DAVE TANGUAY—COLORIST

ALL DAY LONG, FRED'S FEET ARE PUT THROUGH THEIR PACES--

--DRIVING TO WORK--

--TRUDGING ACROSS SUN-BAKED *GRAVEL* AT THE QUARRY--

--SLIDING DOWN THE *RO GH* HIDE OF A DINO--

--TIPPY-TOEING DOWN THE BOWLING ALLEY--

--UNTIL AT LAST...

SCREECH

ARGH! MY FEET ARE *KILLING* ME!!

UNFORTUNATELY, MR. FLINTSTONE, YOU'LL HAVE TO STAY OFF YOUR FEET *ENTIRELY* UNTIL THE TOURNAMENT.

PERHAPS YOUR FAMILY AND FRIENDS WILL PITCH IN SO THAT YOU CAN GET YOUR REST.

SURE!

GEE, THANKS, GANG.

SAY, THIS IS THE *LIFE!* WILMA STAYS HOME AND *TAKES CARE* OF ME, WHILE *BETTY* HANDLES ALL MY CHORES AROUND THE HOUSE!

BARNEY DOES MY *JOB* AT THE QUARRY, DINO BRINGS ME MY PAPER, AND — AW, PEBBLY-POO! DON'T YOU MAKE THE CUTEST LITTLE *TV TRAY!* I COULD GET USED TO THIS!

SEVERAL DAYS LATER...

HOW ARE FRED'S FEET, WILMA?

BETTER. *I'M* THE ONE WHO'S TIRED FROM WAITING ON HIM HAND AND... ER... *FOOT.*

WILMA!!

EXCUSE ME, BETTY. I HAVE TO GO SEE WHAT *HIS HIGHNESS* WANTS.

YES, FRED. ⇒PANT⇐ WHAT IS IT? ⇒HUFF HUFF⇐

CAN YOU HAND ME THE REMOTE? I CAN'T REACH IT.

CERTAINLY, *DEAR.*

THANK GOODNESS THE DOCTOR'S COMING TODAY!

SOON...

GOOD NEWS, EVERYONE! FRED'S FEET HAVE *HEALED.* HE SHOULD HAVE *NO TROUBLE* BOWLING IN THE TOURNAMENT TOMORROW.

JUST IN TIME! LET'S GO RIGHT OVER TO THE BOWLING ALLEY TO PRACTICE!

37

LATER THAT NIGHT...

I'M AFRAID YOU'VE GOT WHAT IS COMMONLY KNOWN AS *BOWLER'S ELBOW.* YOU'LL HAVE TO REST FOR ANOTHER WEEK!

WELL, THERE GOES THE TOURNAMENT.

YEAH, BUT HERE COMES ANOTHER WEEK OF "REST."

BETTY, BARNEY, WOULD YOU...?

SORRY, FRED, WE'RE BUSY FOR THE NEXT WEEK.

WILMA, PEBBLES, COULD YOU...

GET IT *YOURSELF,* FRED!

MMMPH!

DINO, OLD PAL, YOU'LL HELP ME, WON'T YOU? GO GET THE PAPER!

ATTA BOY, DINO! BRING IT HERE!

YEEOW!!

CRUNCH

HEH-HEH-HEH!

OH, *BROTHER!*

THE END

OFF TO WORK

Fred and Barney are just about to start a hard day's work at the quarry. In what order should they pick up these seven pickaxes, taking the top one each time? The answer is at the bottom of the page.

JOHNNY LOVES JOHNNY

Who does Johnny Bravo think he is? Below are a few words that he has chosen to describe what he is. They are all hidden in the wordsquare and read up, down, forwards, backwards and diagonally. When you've found them all, see if you can find the name of the epitome of studliness himself!

HANDSOME	IRRESISTIBLE
GIRL MAGNET	SMART
BEAUTIFUL	GOD'S GIFT
COOL	MAGNIFICENT
STRONG	HUNKY
MUSCLY	LOOKER
INTELLIGENT	BRAVE
FIT	MACHO
STUNNING	WONDERFUL
ADONIS	JOHNNY BRAVO

M	A	C	H	O	J	E	V	A	R	B	E
A	M	F	E	M	O	S	D	N	A	H	L
G	U	C	W	P	H	G	M	U	G	F	B
N	S	R	O	U	N	N	B	A	I	Z	I
I	C	E	N	T	N	I	E	T	R	S	T
F	L	K	D	F	Y	N	A	S	L	T	S
I	Y	O	E	I	B	N	U	I	M	R	I
C	H	O	R	G	R	U	T	N	A	O	S
E	O	L	F	S	A	T	I	O	G	N	E
N	R	O	U	D	V	S	F	D	N	G	R
T	A	W	L	O	O	E	U	A	E	L	R
C	T	N	E	G	I	L	L	E	T	N	I

CHICKEN, EVEN *YOU* CAN'T BE SO SELFISH AS TO NOT UNDERSTAND THE !IMPORTANCE OF RECYCLING!

I AM *NOT A SHELL FISH!*

THIS IS NO TIME TO JOKE, CHICKEN! THE EARTH IS BEING BURIED BENEATH TONS OF GARBAGE EVERY DAY. THE TEACHER SAID THAT IF WE DON'T RECYCLE SOON, EVERYTHING WILL BE *COVERED* BY GARBAGE!

THAT WOULD BE *COOL!*

WE COULD LIVE IN TUNNELS AND BE LIKE THE MOLE PEOPLES IN *ATTACK OF THE MOLE PEOPLES!*

WE HAVE TO DO OUR PART AND RECYCLE AS MUCH AS WE CAN, SO THAT THERE WILL BE TREES AND FORESTS AND ALUMINUM CANS FOR FUTURE GENERATIONS!

WOULD YOU LIKE SOME GUM, CHICKEN?

SURE!

SNATCH!

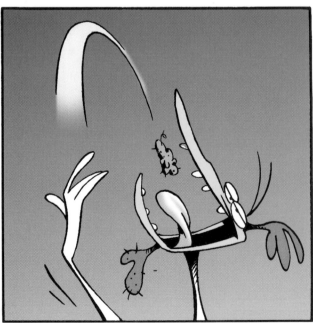

SKA-
RUNCH!

TINCKLE!
TINKLE!

COW, YOU IS DISGUSTING! JUST BECAUSE YOU CHEW YOUR MEALS OVER AND OVER, DON'T MEAN EVERYONE WANTS TO!

BUT IT'S RECYCLING, CHICKEN, IT'S IMPORTANT!

I DON'T CARE 'BOUT NO RECYCLING!

BUT, CHICKEN, THE TEACHER SAID...

I DON'T CARE WHAT NO TEACHER SAID!

BUT CHICKEN--

NO BUTS!

--YOU CAN GET A NICKEL FOR EVERY CAN YOU TURN IN!

FOR REAL?

LATER... COW IS SO STUPID! WHY DIDN'T SHE TELL ME THE ONLY PLACE I COULD GET MONEY FOR DEM EMPTY CANS WUZ AT THE JUNKMANZ?

IT'S GOING TO TAKE *FOREVER* TO GET THAT MANY CANS AGAIN!

I COULD FIND A LOT *MORE* CANS IF I HAD SOME HELP.

HEY, CHICKEN, WHATCHA DOING?

FLEM, EARL, I AM ON A MISSION, AND THAT MISSION ENDS WITH ME...ER, I MEAN WITH *US*, SITTING ON A BRAND NEW, BAD-TO-THE-BONE, CUSTOM CHERRY MINI-BIKE! WIF FLAMES PAINTED ON THE GAS TANK AND EVERY-THING!

SOON... I DONE FOUND ANOTHER ONE, CHICKEN!

ME TOO, CHICKEN, ME TOO!

48

NOW IT'S TIME TO GIVE THE JUNKMAN HIS DUE!

CERBERUS, TAKE THEM TO THE FURNACE!

YOU'RE IN--

--BIG TROUBLE--

--NOW!

CHICKEN, WHAT'S GONNA HAPPEN?

OUR DAYS IS NUMBERED!

AH, WHAT COULD HE DO TO US?

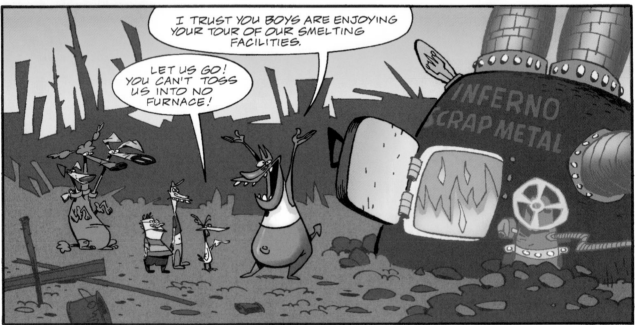

I TRUST YOU BOYS ARE ENJOYING YOUR TOUR OF OUR SMELTING FACILITIES.

LET US GO! YOU CAN'T TOSS US INTO NO FURNACE!

INFERNO SCRAP METAL

TOSS YOU IN THE FURNACE? OF COURSE NOT! BUT I DO NEED YOU TO FEED IT, SO--

--START SHOVELING!

REMEMBER--

--HE LIKES IT--

--HOT!

WHO'S THAT GIRL?

There's one Wacky Racer who beats Dastardly and Muttley every time. Take the first letter of each of the objects below, then rearrange them to find out who it is. The answer is at the bottom of the page.

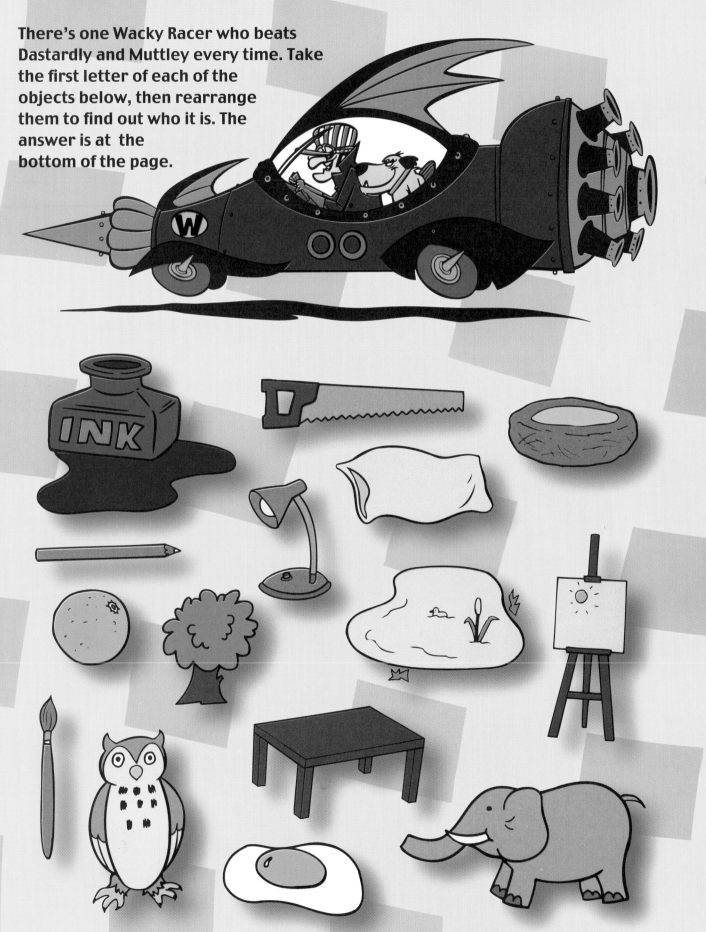

57

HUBBLE BUBBLE

Dexter is hard at work in his lab, creating one of his mystery formulas so that he can be a famous scientist when he grows up. Hidden in the bubbles are the names of four famous scientists, reading forwards or backwards. Can you find all four? The answers are at the bottom of the page.

58

JERRY & TUFFY

Chocolate cake.

Chocolate ice-cream.

Strawberry mousse.

Lemon sponge.

Strawberry ice-cream.

Swiss roll.

Look at all those sweets, Tuffy!

"SWEET TOOTH"
by OSCAR MARTIN

How can humans eat all that?

I've got an idea that'll help us win some pennies.

I told you it was to be a success.

You're really clever!

I'll have one, too!

Calm down, boys. There's more than enough for everybody.

Cheese cake.

Cheese ice-cream.

Cheese cream.

Cheese mousse.

All the girls will have their eyes just on me at the neighbourhood's party today.

Really? I bet they'll also have their eyes on this!

Is this the price? It's cheaper than a match!

One must know how to buy. It was a bargain!

Sometimes bargains don't give good results.

I beg your pardon, but this is a first class suit.

It might be a first-class suit, but yours is a second class brain and girls only like intelligent guys.

MIRROR, MIRROR

Johnny Bravo always has to make sure he's looking good for the girls, so he likes to have plenty of mirrors handy. How many can you spot altogether in his room? The answer is at the bottom of the page.

Answer: There are 10 mirrors altogether. This boy is vain!

GOLD DIGGERS

Top-Cat, Benny and Brain have gone to a rich neighbourhood to see what treasures they can find in the bins. One cat has struck gold – which one? The answer is at the bottom of the page.

Answer: Benny is the lucky cat!

JETSON, I'VE BEEN REVIEWING YOUR RECORD, AND SEEING HOW MANY TIMES YOU'VE BUNGLED, FOULED UP, FLUBBED, AND ERRED, I'M VERY, VERY, VERY--

--PROUD OF THE WORK YOU'VE DONE LATELY. YOU'VE GONE AN ENTIRE WEEK WITHOUT A SINGLE MISTAKE. KEEP IT UP, AND YOU MAY BE UP FOR A PROMOTION!

OH, THANK YOU, SIR! I WON'T LET YOU DOWN!

JETSON! LOOK OUT FOR THAT--

WARNING! WARNING! OVERLOAD! OVERLOAD!

--LEVER.

YOU NINCOMPOOP! YOU'VE RESET THE SPROCKETS ON THE MASTER DISPOSOTRON, WHICH CONTROLS ALL THE WASTE DISPOSAL UNITS IN THE CITY! WHO KNOWS WHAT ENVIRONMENTAL CATASTROPHE THIS MAY CAUSE!

JETSON, YOU'RE FIRED!!!

WASN'T IT YOU WHO CALLED ME A POMPOUS WINDBAG, AN ARROGANT BLOWHARD, A SANCTIMONIOUS IGNORAMUS, AND A STUPIDHEAD?

WELL, YES... BUT IT WAS ONLY IN THE SPIRIT OF FRIENDLY COMPETITION. HEH-HEH.

SO, THE ONLY WAY TO RESET THE SPROCKETS OF THE MASTER DISPOSOTRON IS TO REPLACE THE COG, WHICH *I* MANUFACTURE. VERY INTERESTING.

I'LL TELL YOU WHAT... FOR — I DON'T KNOW — 51 PERCENT OWNERSHIP OF SPACELY SPROCKETS—

—I JUST MIGHT THINK IT OVER.

THIS IS BLACKMAIL!

I PREFER TO CALL IT FREE ENTERPRISE. NOW, BARK LIKE A DOG, OR I WON'T HELP YOU!

OH, HELLO, JETSON! COULD YOU CLEAN THESE ASHES UP?

SURE THING, BOSS!

ARF! ARF! ARF!

ZAP

WHAT'S GOING ON HERE?!

THE ROCK EXCHANGE

Pebbles and Bam-Bam have been collecting coloured rocks. If Pebbles gives Bam-Bam 3 of her pink rocks for each one of his yellow rocks, how many should he give her so that they both have the same amount of rocks? The answer is at the bottom of the page.

Answer: Bam-Bam should give Pebbles 3 of his yellow rocks in exchange for 9 of her pink rocks so that they each have 15 rocks altogether.

MYSTERY TOUR

Scooby and his friends are on another assignment to investigate a mysterious phenomenon: the spirit of a clown has been haunting the local fairground and scaring away its customers. Jump aboard the Mystery Machine to drive round the fairground and help the gang to find the villain behind the mask.

Scooby can't resist hot dogs! Miss a go to take a snack.

Daphne spot teller. Miss she pays

Someone's tailing you! Speed on two squares.

Foiled by a smoke bomb! Reverse back two squares.

All you need to play are a counter for each player and a dice. You need to throw a six to get into the fair. Work your way round the fairground by taking turns to throw the dice. You must throw the exact number to land on the final square and unmask the culprit. Then you're the winner!

You take a short cut behind the Big Wheel. Go on two spaces.

AND I WOULD HAVE GOTTEN AWAY WITH IT, IF THOSE NOSY KIDS HAD MINDED THEIR OWN CANDY FLOSS!

All the lights fuse. Miss a go while Velma fixes them.

THE FLINTSTONES -IN- CAVE-AT EMPTOR!

WRITER: SAM HENDERSON
ARTIST: STEPHANIE GLADDEN
LETTERER: PHIL FELIX
COLORIST: DAVE TANGUAY
ASSISTANT: MIKE BRISBOIS
EDITOR: BRONWYN TAGGART

HI, EVERYONE! WELCOME TO ANOTHER EPISODE OF "I CAN'T BELIEVE IT'S TRUE!" I'M YOUR HOST, *DICK VAN PATSTONE*--

--AND HAVE I GOT AN *AMAZING* INVENTION FOR *YOU!*

I CAN'T BELIEVE IT'S TRUE!

HI, DICK!

HOW MANY TIMES HAVE YOU SAID TO YOURSELF, "*BOY,* I *HATE* GOING TO THE BARBERSHOP! IT'S OUT OF THE WAY, AND HOW DO I KNOW THE BARBER WON'T *STEAL MY WALLET?*"

THOSE WERE THE WORRIES OF *YESTERDAY,* FOLKS! IN THESE *MODERN* TIMES, *YOU* CAN CUT YOUR HAIR IN THE *PRIVACY OF YOUR OWN HOME*--

--WITH *THE HAIRMASTER!*

OOH!

AAH!

AS YOU CAN SEE, I'M A LITTLE TOO *THIN* ON *TOP* TO USE ONE MYSELF. IS THERE ANYONE WHO'D LIKE TO *TRY* THIS WONDER OF TECHNOLOGY?

WHY, *YES!* I JUST HAPPEN TO BE PASSING BY, AND I WAS *THINKING* I NEED A TRIM, BUT I'D DO *ANYTHING* TO AVOID THOSE LONG, TEDIOUS *BARBERSHOP* VISITS!

NOW *OBSERVE*, LADIES AND GENTLEMEN, HOW *EASY* THIS IS...

OOH!

SHLOOW!

AAH!

CHOMP!

THIS FANTASTIC NEW ITEM CAN BE YOURS FOR THREE EASY PAYMENTS OF $99.99. JUST CALL THE NUMBER ON YOUR SCREEN AND HAVE YOUR CREDIT CARD READY!

TWO WEEKS LATER...

'BYE, WILMA, HONEY. I'M OFF TO GET A HAIRCUT!

NO, FRED! NOT AT ONE OF THOSE CROOKED BARBERSHOPS!

I'VE GOT A SURPRISE FOR YOU, DEAR. CLOSE YOUR EYES!

THIS BETTER BE GOOD, WILMA!

IT'S IMPORTANT FOR ME TO KEEP MY HAIR SHORT, WHICH IS WHY I WAS ON MY WAY TO THE BARBER, AND WHY I HOPE THIS SURPRISE IS QUICK...!

WILMA, WHAT ARE YOU DOING?

SHLOOW!

HEY!

OW!

WHAT TH--?

SHLOOW!

GET IT OFF ME! GET IT OFF!

CHOMP CHOMP!

THE NEXT DAY...

HEY, FRED. HOW COME YOU'RE WEARING YOUR WATER BUFFALO HELMET TO WORK?

ER...Um—IT'S PART OF MY HAZING.

BUT YOU'VE BEEN A MEMBER FOR TEN YEARS!

WELL, I...UH...

TIME CLO...

OKAY, IF YOU MUST KNOW—MY HEAD IS ALL SCRATCHED UP BECAUSE MY WIFE BOUGHT ME ONE OF THOSE STUPID HAIR-MASTERS FROM A STUPID TV COMMERCIAL!

Heh heh heh

GEE, SORRY, FRED! BUT YOU GOTTA ADMIT YOUR CRANIUM SURE LOOKS FUNNY!

Uh huh huh huh huh huh huh huh huh

Huh

Huh

ER, I'M NOT FEELING WELL...

LATER...

IT'S A MILD CASE OF FOOD POISONING, MISTER RUBBLE! YOU HAD BITS OF TORTOISE SCALP IN YOUR STOMACH. YOU'LL BE FINE IN AN HOUR OR TWO.

BUT, DOC! THAT'S IMPOSSIBLE! I'VE HAD NOTHING BUT JUICE ALL WEEK! UNLESS...

MEANWHILE...

MY BARNEY'S BEEN LOOKING PRETTY *HEALTHY* SINCE I PUT HIM ON A *JUICE DIET*. THIS *JUICE-MASTER* IS GREAT!

MAYBE YOU SHOULD GET ONE FOR FRED.

OH, YOU KNOW *FRED*. HE'LL DIET WHEN THERE'S A COLD DAY IN --

--HELLO, BARNEY!

YOU BOYS ARE HOME EARLY!

BETTY! WILMA! DON'T DRINK THAT *JUICE!*

YEAH! OUR *JUICER'S* GOT *DANDRUFF!*

WHERE'D YOU GET THIS THING, ANYWAY?

DICK VAN PATSTONE ADVERTISED IT ON HIS "I CAN'T BELIEVE IT'S TRUE" SHOW.

OH, DEAR! THOSE ARE THE *SAME PEOPLE* WHO SOLD ME THAT CRUMMY HAIR-MASTER!

IF ONLY THERE WERE A WAY TO GET EVEN WITH THOSE THIEVES!

I'LL GET THAT!

KNOCK KNOCK!

82

GOOD EVENING! I REPRESENT THE PRODUCERS OF "I CAN'T BELIEVE IT'S TRUE." WE'RE DOING A SHOW IN *YOUR* TOWN, AND GIVING AWAY *TICKETS* DOOR-TO-DOOR...

YOU *CROOKS!* YOU CAN *TAKE* YOUR TICKETS AND --

IXNAY, FRED! THIS IS OUR *CHANCE!*

--AND GIVE US *FOUR* OF THEM!

I'VE GOT A *GREAT* IDEA! HUDDLE AROUND AND I'LL TELL YOU ALL ABOUT IT!

ACROSS TOWN...

THIS IS A GREAT *RACKET*, EH, BOSS? WE BUY UNTRAINED ANIMALS CHEAP AND FOIST 'EM ON AN UNSUSPECTING PUBLIC!

YEP!

MISTER VAN PATSTONE, YOU'RE ON IN ONE MINUTE!

QUICK! PUT ON THIS FAKE BEARD!

HI, I'M DICK VAN PATSTONE! TODAY WE HAVE A VERY SPECIAL GUEST WHO USED TO WEIGH OVER THREE HUNDRED POUNDS! TELL ME, SIR! HOW DID YOU LOSE ALL THAT WEIGHT?

I CAN'T BELIEVE IT'S TRUE!

WITH THIS INCREDIBLE NEW INVENTION, THE *THIGHBUILDER!* JUST FIVE MINUTES A DAY TAKES IT OFF IN NO TIME! *OBSERVE--*

LOOK HOW EASY THIS IS! DO WE HAVE ANY *QUESTIONS* FROM THE AUDIENCE?

YOU THINK *THIS* JOB'S TOUGH, YOU OUGHTA MEET MY *BROTHER,* THE *BUTTBUILDER!*

YES! HOW DO YOU *SLEEP* AT NIGHT KNOWING YOU MAKE FAULTY PRODUCTS?

ER... SHE'S NOT ONE OF OUR "*PLANTS,*" IS SHE?

MY HUSBAND AND I BOUGHT A *HAIRMASTER* FROM YOUR SHOW, AND *LOOK* AT HIM!

LET'S SEE HOW *YOU* LIKE USING IT!

HEY!

SHE'S RIGHT! I'VE BOUGHT SHODDY MERCHANDISE FROM THAT MAN AS WELL!

CHOMP CHOMP!

ME, TOO!

YEAH!

AAGH! EEH!

HOW DO *YOU* LIKE DRINKING FROM A MACHINE WITH *FLAKY SKIN?*

⸫GLUGH!⸪

YEAH! AND I'M *SOOO SURE* YOU USE YOUR VENOMOUS WATER MASSAGER ALL THE TIME!

YOUR *BLENDER* TRIED TO *EAT* MY PET SABERTOOTH!

OKAY! OKAY! YOU'RE RIGHT!

I GIVE UP!

BITE!

SPIT!

CRUNCH!

CHOMP!

AND FINALLY, INFOMERCIAL SPOKESMAN DICK VAN PATSTONE TURNED HIMSELF IN TO THE POLICE FOR SELLING BAD MERCHANDISE.

THAT'S THE NEWS, AND GOOD NIGHT.

NEW

COMING UP NEXT, A PAID PROGRAM ABOUT MAKING MONEY IN REAL ESTATE...

HERE WE GO AGAIN...!

THE END!

DEXTER'S LAB LOG

After countless exposures to **BIOTOMIC ENERGY,** all testing proves **NEGATIVE.** ☑

No enhanced abilities.

No physical mutations.

NO *NOTHING.* IT SEEMS YOU SHALL NEVER BECOME ANYTHING MORE THAN A MERE *MONKEY.*

MONKEY— HEAR MY THOUGHTS.

THIS IS *AGENT HONEYDEW.* THE EARTH'S IN *TROUBLE.* WE NEED YOU, MONKEY!

DIAL M FOR MONKEY

GENNDY TARTAKOVSKY / PAUL RUDISH
STORY

PAUL RUDISH
PENCILS

PAT BROSSEAU
LETTERER

BARBARA KRUEGER
INKS

PAUL RUDISH
COLORIST

BRONWYN TAGGART
EDITOR

OBJECT ENTERING EARTH'S ATMOS-PHERE--

400 KILO-METERS AND CLOSING --

300

200

100

50

20, 10, 5, 2--

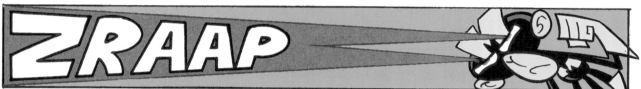

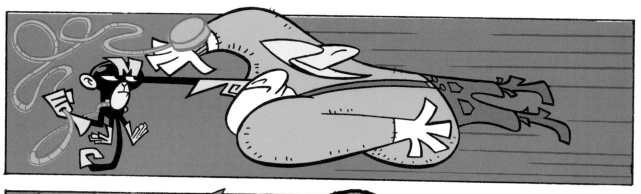

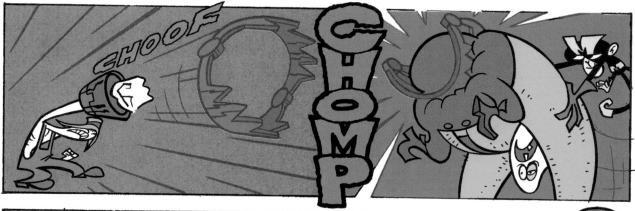

PICK UP A PIC-A-NIC!

Yogi's feeling a little peckish. Show him and Boo Boo which route through the park will give them the most pic-a-nic baskets – and watch out for Ranger Smith! See the bottom of the page for the answer.

Answer: Route B has the most pic-a-nic baskets.

OUT *THERE*, THERE'S TOO MUCH NOISE! ALL THOSE PEOPLE WITH THEIR CARS AND RADIOS, AND MACHINES WITH THEIR BANGING AND THEIR CLANGING!

ZOOOM

HONK HONK

BEEP

RAT TAT TAT

RAT TAT TAT

EVERYWHERE IS *NOISE NOISE* **NOISE!** I JUST WANNA--

HEY, IS THAT KEY LIME PIE?

IT SURE IS, MY FRIEND!

COULD I HAVE JUST ONE BITE?

I DON'T SEE WHY NOT!

Mmm... I LOVE PIE! THE ONLY THINGS I GET TO EAT IN HERE ARE NUTS AND BERRIES.

AW, THAT STUFF'S FOR ANIMALS.

SAY, I'VE GOT A BUSINESS PROPOSITION FOR YOU. COME OUTSIDE.

Uh-oh, I SEE TROUBLE COMING.

CHOMP!

THERE ARE A LOT OF PIC-A-NIC BASKETS OUT THERE LYING AROUND, AND ALMOST EVERY ONE'S GOT A DELICIOUS PIE. NOW, BOO BOO AND I CAN'T GET ALL OF THEM BY OURSELVES. WE COULD USE A LITTLE HELP.

I'D BE HAPPY TO HELP YOU! WITH THEIR FOOD GONE, PEOPLE WILL LEAVE THIS PARK AND I'LL HAVE PEACE AND QUIET!

GREAT! WE'LL SPLIT THE PROCEEDS FIFTY-FIFTY!

THERE'S A FAMILY OVER THERE! I'LL DISTRACT THEM WHILE YOU TAKE THE LOOT!

I'M STAYING OVER HERE!

HEY, LOOK! THAT BEAR'S DOING THE MACARENA!

GEE, YOU'RE SWELL!

CAN YOU DO THE MASHED POTATO?

LOOK AT HIM GO!

THIS IS FUN!

HOW'D I SAY WE'D SPLIT IT AGAIN? SIXTY-FORTY?

OR WAS IT SEVENTY-THIRTY?

I DON'T LIKE THIS, YOGI...

I DIDN'T DO IT, RANGER SMITH! WHATEVER IT WAS, I DIDN'T DO IT!

RELAX, YOGI. THIS IS A FRIENDLY VISIT!

RANGER, COULD YOU READ THIS BOOK TO US?

SORRY, I REALLY DON'T HAVE THE TIME.

BESIDES, I'VE HEARD THIS BOOK'S TERRIBLE! SOME STORY ABOUT TWO BEARS WHO TEACH AN OLD MAN TO ENJOY LIFE. WHAT A LOAD OF HOOEY!

LIFE'S RICH PIC-A-NIC BASKET by VLADIMIR FITZPATRICK

ANYHOO, I CAME HERE TO TELL YOU THAT I'M GOING ON VACATION. I'M OFF TO HAWAII! FOR A WEEK!

BUT WHO'S GONNA PROTECT US POOR WOODLAND CREATURES?

YOU'LL HAVE A REPLACEMENT RANGER! ALOHA!

BUT YOGI, WHAT ARE WE GONNA DO WITHOUT THE RANGER?

I KNOW WHAT I'M GONNA DO, MY LITTLE URSINE URCHIN!

I'M GONNA HAVE PLENTY OF PIC-A-NICS!

HEY!

SNAG!

FOOD FIGHT

Yogi and Boo Boo have emptied out a pic-a-nic basket and are looking forward to tucking into a feast. There's two of everything...with one exception! Which piece of food will the bears be fighting over? The answer is at the bottom of the page.

Answer: There is only one pie - tough luck, Boo Boo!